WHAT ON EARTH?

Arctic

BART AND LYNN KING

High Noon Books
Novato, California

Editor: Michael Milone
Interior Illustrations: Cynthia Coverston
Cover Design: Bonni Gatter

International Standard Book Number: 978-1-57128-503-4

18 17 16 15 14 13 12 11 10 09
10 09 08 07 06 05 04 03 02 01

You will enjoy all the High Noon Books.
Write for a free full list of titles or visit us at
www.HighNoonBooks.com.

Contents

1. Cold on Hold 1
2. Dress for Mess.....................................6
3. Nice Ice 11
4. Terns and Ferns..............................18
5. News Crew 26
6. Cracks and Tracks 29
7. Gale Tale...37

CHAPTER 1

Cold on Hold

Nate, Val, and Sam were on Val's porch. They were talking about Tess. "Where is she again?" Sam asked. Val sighed. She got up and said she would be right back. The screen door slammed. It was Val again. She held a globe of the world in her hands.

Val sat down next to her friends. She pointed to a line near the top of the globe. "Do you see this line?" she asked Sam. "Tess is somewhere north of it. The line is the Arctic Circle."

It was true. Tess was in the Arctic! And they were stuck here at home. Boy, did they wish they could be with her! Tess's Aunt Kate had work in the Far North. She studied where birds flew. Two or three times each year, Aunt Kate went to a lab there. This time, she asked Tess to join her.

Tess was thrilled and said yes. When she told her friends, they were glad, too. The Arctic would be a good place to make their next film. But now Tess was gone. They were not sure what to do. Nate pulled out his laptop. Nate would see if she had sent any news. He found an e-mail from her. The four friends read what Tess had to say.

The Arctic is so cool! The plane flight was way too long. But once we got here, it was worth the trip.

I thought there would be lots of snow here. But there is only a little snow on the ground now. That is because we are in the south part of the Arctic. Right now it is past the warm part of the year. Warm here is not the same as warm back home. Warm in this place is a cool 37 to 54 degrees

Aunt Kate and I have our own room here at the lab. It is late at night now, and it

3

is dark out. But it is not always dark at night here. In the summer, the sun shines even at night. It's a good thing it is dark now. If it were light, I would have a hard time going to sleep!

I plan to send video files to you at the end of each day. When I get back home, we can look at them together. I can tell you then what each video shows.

Tess

After reading the note, the three friends looked at each other. They were both sad and glad. They were happy to hear from Tess. But they also felt left out. What was their part in this new film about the Arctic? Did they have to wait for Tess to come home before they could get started?

None of them wanted to sit still while Tess had all the fun. They would not put their film about the cold on hold. Val spoke up first. She would make a list of animals that Tess could look for. Nate would do a list of plants. When it was Sam's turn, he said, "You will see."

CHAPTER 2

Dress for Mess

The next day, Tess got dressed fast. It was cold in the room. She could see her own breath. Tess planned to be out all day. She put on clothes that would keep her warm. There were tights, wool socks, a shirt with long sleeves, and warm pants. Over that she wore a thick coat, a hat with soft ear flaps, a pair of gloves, and a pair of boots. She tied her boots, and then her aunt woke up.

Aunt Kate laughed. "Wow! Are you sure

this is your first trip to the Arctic? You really know how to dress for the cold," she said.

They went to get something to eat. On the way, Aunt Kate told Tess about her plans for the day. First she would visit the people here who tracked birds. Aunt Kate wanted Tess to meet them and to learn about their jobs. Next, Aunt Kate would show Tess around the lab. This place was not just a bird lab. The folks here did other things, too. If a big storm came along, they would see it first. Then they could warn other people.

People ate here together in a room called a mess hall. A cook made three meals each day. The whole group knew Aunt Kate. They were shocked that she brought a girl on this trip. "This is my niece, Tess," said Aunt Kate. "She and three friends make films. Her new film will be about the Arctic." Tess felt shy at first. She soon got over it. She wanted to learn many things from these folks. All of them had a lot to teach her.

One man's name was Gabe. He had worked in the Arctic for years. His job was to look at the many animals and plants. He studied how they could live with so much cold and so little sun. Tess was stumped. So little sun? She knew there were days when the sun did not set. It seemed there was too much sun up here!

Gabe said that in summer, the sun could be

up as late as midnight. But there are many more cold months. Winters are dark. There is very little sun. A little north of here, there is less sun. In winter, it sets and does not come up again for almost three months!

As Gabe talked, Tess looked out the window. She could see a patch of brown grass here and there. Even if she did not see them, she knew there were bears, deer, moose, hare, and other animals out there. But the bit of grass was the only plant she saw. Gabe read Tess's mind. "How many plants do you think live here?" he asked.

Tess shrugged and said, "I don't know. Maybe 100?"

Gabe shook his head. "Try 17 times that," he said. "There are about 1,700 plants here. And 900 of those plants bloom around the same time."

Tess thought this would be fun to see. Flowers in the Arctic!

CHAPTER 3

Nice Ice

Back at home, Nate, Val, and Sam had done some work. It was time to share their notes. They would send Tess a list of things to look for. Sam said, "Let's meet at my house. I have a plan."

It was a nice day, so the three sat outdoors. Nate pulled out his blue notebook and opened it. He could not wait to tell his two friends what he had learned. Nate had looked on the Internet. He found out about the lab where Tess was

11

staying. It was in a flat part of the Arctic called the tundra. "The plants that grow in the tundra are strong," he said. Only strong plants could live in such a cold place with so little sun for much of the year!

Nate said that the plants were small, too. "They grow low to the ground," he said. "There are trees, too. You would not know them if you saw them." They look more like shrubs because they are so small.

Sam and Val wanted to know what kind of plants Tess might see. Nate was not sure. If the big snows had not started, she might see some grass and some moss. She might find some odd plants that grew on rocks.

It was too bad Tess could not be there in the short summer. "Much of the Arctic thaws at that time. Much of the snow melts," said Nate. More than half of the place has no snow then. The land is wet from the melted snow. Plants there must make the most of a short growing time. He told them how the plants soak up the bright sun and bloom all at once. Their seeds grow ripe fast. The seeds must spread before it gets cold again.

"Here is something I bet you did not know," said Sam. "There are a lot of bugs where Tess is." Nate and Val did not think this could be right. "Bugs love wet places," Sam said. "When the snow melts, it leaves pools of water.

The bugs lay eggs in the water."

"I bet Tess is glad that she missed the warm part of the year," said Val. "She does not have to deal with all those bugs." Val then told them what she had found.

Val found out that some Arctic animals could change their color. One of these is the snowshoe hare. A hare is a kind of rabbit. In the warm months, the snow is gone. The hare's fur is brown to match the land. In the cold months, snow is on the ground. The hare's fur turns white. The same is true of a fox that lives up north. This trick helps these animals hide and not be seen.

There were other animals that Val hoped

Tess could catch on film. A kind of deer lives up north. Val thought the fur facts were very cool. Each hair in this deer's fur is like a tiny tube. Air is trapped inside each tube of hair. This air helps to keep the deer warm. The deer move in herds and eat the grass that grows in the tundra.

There are moose and musk oxen up there, too. Val showed Sam and Nate a drawing she had made of a musk ox. An ox looks like a big cow. It has horns that start at the top of its head. They curve down each side. The tips turn up at each end like a funny hair flip.

It seemed like a good time to take a break. Sam stood up. He said he would be right back,

Val showed Sam and Nate a drawing she had made of a musk ox.

and he was. He brought a box of ice cream, three bowls, and three spoons. "All this talk about the cold and the snow made me think of a nice kind of ice. Want some?"

Val said, "I bet this was your plan all along!"

CHAPTER 4

Terns and Ferns

Tess left the mess hall with Aunt Kate. They walked to the room where Kate and her team did their work. The birds they track are called terns. Terns are sea birds. They are good fliers. Each year, terns fly from the north part of Earth all the way to the south part. The birds fly about 24,000 miles each year. It is the longest flight path of any bird.

Terns are not big or small. They are somewhere in between. Their bodies are 13 to

15 inches long. Their wings are 26 to 30 inches across. The birds are mostly white. A tern has a red beak, red feet, and a black cap. Terns come north to lay their eggs. The eggs hatch when it is warm. When the sun and the warm days are gone, they fly south again.

The terns were gone for the year by now. But the nesting grounds were not too far from the lab. This was where the terns laid their eggs. The nests would still be there. Tess asked if they could go and see the nests. Her aunt said, "That's a good idea." They grabbed their coats and headed out.

This was the first time Tess had been out all day. The cold air on her face was a shock.

The birds are mostly white. A tern has a red beak, red feet, and a black cap.

The skin on her face grew stiff. When she breathed, the air hurt her lungs. She was not used to such cold!

Aunt Kate led Tess to the nesting place. The birds were all gone. There was no need to worry about scaring them or their babies. Tess had her video camera. There was not much to film. Tess kneeled down. She could see the soft dents in the ground. These were old nests. Some of them were lined with grass. Bits and pieces of shell were on the ground. The shells were the same color as the ground. Tess knew that this helped to keep the eggs safe from animals.

The two of them walked back to the mess hall for lunch. After that, Tess went with Gabe to his part of the lab. Tess told Gabe about where they had just been. "I wish Aunt Kate and I had come sooner," she said. "That way, I could have shot some film of the birds."

Gabe smiled. "I have just the thing for you," he said. They sat down at a desk. Gabe had a laptop computer. Gabe clicked on a file name that said BIRDS and opened it. He clicked on another file name that said TERNS. A short video started. It was a film of the nesting place in summer. It was filled with terns and their eggs! There was sound, too. The terns were making a lot of noise. They had a very loud call. "I used a zoom and kept as far away as I could," said Gabe. "But the birds saw me and were not pleased."

Tess looked at the list of files in Gabe's BIRDS folder. There were swans, ducks, gulls, loons, and owls. She asked Gabe if the film was shot near the lab. He said most of it was not. Gabe went to all kinds of places. The lab was like his base camp. To Tess, the lab seemed very strange. There were no shops or malls or schools near it. There were no homes or roads for miles. She and Aunt Kate had to take a plane to get there. How did Gabe get from place to place?

"Sometimes I fly," said Gabe. "But that is only for very long trips. I ride in a dog sled, too. And I use these a lot." Gabe lifted one foot and then the other. "Just like a man long ago, John Rae."

John Rae was one of Gabe's heroes. He lived about 150 years ago. Rae made three trips to the Arctic. He went to find a man who was lost. Rae never found the man. On his trips, he mapped more than 1,500 miles of coast. He walked more than 23,000 miles. "He did not have cold feet when it came to Arctic walking," said Gabe with a laugh.

Tess spent the next hour looking at the many plant pictures on Gabe's laptop. And Gabe knew the name of each grass, fern, moss, bloom, and shrub. "This is as close as you will get to a plant this time of year," Gabe said. He pointed outside. Tess turned and looked. It was

snowing.

CHAPTER 5

News Crew

Sam was at Nate's house. At first they wanted to work on the film. Val had to go home right after school. Nate and Sam needed Val's help on the film. They decided to just hang out. The two boys were watching TV when news of a storm came on. In the past, the boys did not care much about storms. But a note from Tess had changed the way they thought.

Tess said there was a team at the lab whose main job was to watch for storms. The Arctic

26

was a good place to do this. Many storms start from the north and the west. The storms move to the south and the east. If a strong wind or big storm started, the lab could find out first and warn others.

Nate turned up the sound on the TV. Behind the news crew on the screen, there was a big map. The map showed the path of the storm. It looked like the storm was heading at Tess. Nate and Sam thought maybe Tess's lab sent the story about the storm.

"Do you think Tess is seeing any snow?" asked Sam.

Nate frowned. He said, "It's been a while since we heard from her. Maybe we should try to reach her one more time." Nate seemed a little worried.

CHAPTER 6

Cracks and Tracks

In fact, Tess was seeing a lot of snow. It was falling hard. She had a hard time seeing her own hands as they gripped the side of the dog sled. Who knew such a nice day could turn so bad?

In the morning, Gabe said he was going on a field trip. It had snowed all night but now it was clear. Gabe asked Aunt Kate if it would be OK to take Tess on the field trip. Aunt Kate thought it was a good idea. She wanted Tess to have a chance to see more things before they headed home.

Gabe hired a man with a dog sled to take them. The man was waiting for them outside with his team of dogs. Tess was thrilled when she saw them. There were nine dogs in all. They panted hard. They had run far to reach the lab. The driver was dressed warmly. He had fur pants and a fur coat with a hood. He wore big gloves to keep his hands warm.

Tess climbed on board the sled with Gabe and the driver. In a bit, they were on their way. At first the dogs ran fast, but then they slowed a little. Tess looked at the scene around her. She was glad to get away from the lab. Time was slipping away. She needed to take more videos.

Tess climbed on board the sled with Gabe and the driver.

Sure, Gabe had said she could use his film clips. But she wanted her own clips, too.

The sled dogs spread out in a fan shape. This seemed odd to Tess. She had seen sled dogs in books and on TV. The dogs always ran in two lines, side by side. She asked the driver about this. He said that the fan shape was a good way to run on ice. It spread the weight of the dogs over the ice. Tess nodded. This made sense. She asked when they would be on the ice. Gabe and the driver laughed. "We are on the ice right now," said Gabe.

He then asked the driver to stop. An order to the dogs made them slow to a stop. Tess stepped off the sled. She could not feel her face.

It stung from the cold. Gabe gave her a mask to wear. The mask kept her face warm but she could still see.

Tess asked Gabe how he knew that they were on the ice. "Here is one clue," said Gabe. He pointed to a small hole. He said it was a seal hole. The seals make holes so they can breathe when the sea freezes. They swim in the water and come up to the hole to get air. As the days get colder, the ice gets thicker. But the seals keep the holes open with their teeth and their sharp claws. The seals must take care. Bears loved to eat seals. They knew the holes were a good place to catch a meal.

Tess wanted to film the hole and a seal.

Gabe asked the driver to call the dogs away. If a seal was near, it would hear the dogs move. If the seal thought all of them had left it might come up for some air. The driver and the dogs moved away. Tess and Gabe waited. They held very still and did not speak. A black nose could be seen in the hole, but not for long! Tess filmed the seal before it swam away fast. Tess knew Val would be pleased. Val had put the spotted seal, the ringed seal, and the harp seal on her list. Still, any seal would do if Tess could get it on film.

Just then, there was a loud cracking sound. Far off, a big chunk of ice broke away. Gabe gave Tess a wink. "Do you need any more clues that we are on ice?" he asked. Tess shook her head. The two of them went back to the sled.

Tess learned many things from Gabe. After lunch, he showed her how to know sea ice from fresh water ice. The sea ice was salty. It made shapes that looked like frost blooms. Fresh water ice had no salt. It came from snow that had turned to ice.

Gabe found some tracks in the snow. He told Tess which tracks had come from which animal. The biggest ones were bear tracks. They also found deer and hare tracks. The hare tracks looked like snowshoes. For each set of tracks, Gabe took notes. He wrote where the tracks were found and who made them.

The sky was dark gray. The dog sled and its crew started to turn back. A few snowflakes fell at first. Soon they came down so thick that Tess felt blinded. It was also hard for Gabe and his driver to see. The dogs did their best, but even they seemed lost. For the first time all week, Tess felt afraid. Would they find the lab? Would they have to build some kind of ice house to make it through the night?

CHAPTER 7

Gale Tale

"Are you sure we have the right day and the right time? Is this the right gate?" Nate asked. He, Val, and Sam were waiting for Tess's plane. The plane was late. Val pulled a slip of paper from her bag to check. Yes, this was the spot. Tess and Aunt Kate should have been here by now.

Nate went to talk to the man at the desk. After a while, Nate came back. He told Val and Sam some bad news. There had been a big storm at the place where Tess and Aunt Kate were flying from. No planes had left there in days! It sounded like their friend was stuck. With sad faces, the pals started to walk away from the gate.

"If Mr. Byrd was flying Tess's plane, she would be here by now," said Sam. Nate and Val gave Sam an odd look. Who was Mr. Byrd? This was no time to make a joke. But Sam was not trying to get a laugh. He was talking about Richard Byrd.

"Some say that Byrd was the first to fly over the North Pole," said Sam. That was back in 1926. Today, many planes make this same trip every day."

Val and Nate looked at their friend. When did Sam have time to learn all this?

Just then Nate, Val, and Sam heard a voice calling their names. It sounded like someone they knew well. They turned around and saw Tess. She had left Aunt Kate's side and was running to them. "Boy, am I glad to see you," she said. Tess gave each of them a hug. "I have so much to tell."

Tess told them how she, Gabe, the driver, and his dogs had been caught in a big storm. It was just as she had feared. They could not find their way back to the lab that day. To keep warm and safe through the night, Gabe and the driver built an ice house. They cut big blocks of firm snow. They stacked the blocks to make walls and a roof. They cut out a small door very low to the ground. That way, the heat from their bodies would rise and would not go out the door. That night, Tess, Gabe, and the driver slept in the ice hut.

Sam wanted to know if the dogs had slept in the ice house, too. Tess shook her head. "No," she said. "The dogs rolled up into tight fur balls and slept outside."

The crew at the lab waited for news. "We felt helpless to do anything," said Aunt Kate. "We were very worried." The storm raged on all night. Gabe and the driver hoped the morning would be better. When the sun came up, they

They stacked the blocks to make walls and a roof.

could go to a town that was near. There, they could wait for the storm to calm. They could call the lab and tell Aunt Kate that they were safe.

At dawn, the three of them crawled out of the ice house. They tied the dogs to the sled and took off again. By noon, they could see the dark outline of the town. They were safe at last!

The next day, Aunt Kate met Tess in town. They could fly home from there. But snow was on the ground. They waited for the snow plow. After a few hours, they took off. Both of them were very happy.

Tess's eyes were bright as she ended her story. "Oh, and one more thing," she said. "I got it all on film." Nate, Val, and Sam could not wait to see the video. They were all very glad their friend was safe at home.